IT's ALL ABOUT ME!

A Quiz Book

by Karen Phillips

KLUTZ®

What are you like... really?

To reveal the real you (if you dare) grab this pen and some notepad paper from the back of the book and take these quizzes. Answer everything honestly and don't hold anything back. Give your friends these quizzes, too, and soon you'll know more about each other than anybody ever should.

are you an OPTIMIST?

Navigate the game board to see how optimistic you really are.

START

Which of these colors do you prefer?
- ○ Yellow (move up 1 space)
- ● Blue (move up 2 spaces)

When you get your hair cut, you...
- bring in a magazine picture to show what you want (move up 3 spaces)
- say, "Do whatever you think will look look best" (move up 2 spaces)

Do you ever dream that you're flying?
- Yes (move up 2 spaces)
- No (move up 1 space)

It's raining and you forgot an umbrella. You...
- walk home in the rain (move up 3 spaces)
- ask a friend for a ride (move up 2 spaces)

You're marooned on a desert island. Which would you rather have with you?
- matches and some signal flares (move up 2 spaces)
- matches, fishing stuff and a frying pan (move up 3 spaces)
- a hairdryer (move back 1 space)

The night before a big test, you're more likely to
- sleep like a log (move up 2 spaces)
- toss and turn all night (move up 3 spaces)

ZZ

4

If you could only wear one style of shoe for the rest of your life, which would it be?
- Sneakers (move up 4 spaces)
- flip-flops (move up 1 space)
- Combat boots (move back 1 space)

Seriously now, pick one: This glass is...
- half full (move up 4 spaces)
- half empty (move up 2 spaces)

Which movie would you rather see?
- the one everyone's raving about (move up 2 spaces)
- the one nobody's seen yet (move up 3 spaces)

ADMIT ONE

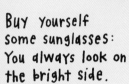

Optimist

Buy yourself some sunglasses: You always look on the bright side.

Half and Half

You're part optimist, part pessimist.

You're a poptimist!

Pessimist

Okay, you're a pessimist, but everything is going to be fine.

Really, it is.

What kind of **cookie**

Are you sweet, spicy or just plain nuts?

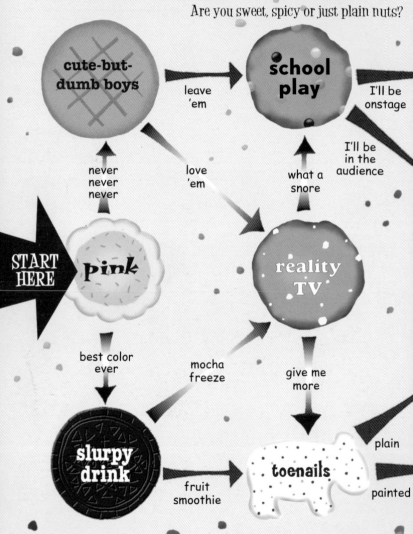

cute-but-dumb boys

school play

leave 'em

I'll be onstage

I'll be in the audience

never never never

love 'em

what a snore

START HERE

pink

reality TV

best color ever

mocha freeze

give me more

slurpy drink

toenails

plain

fruit smoothie

painted

are you?
Follow this chart to find out.

GINGERSNAP

You are a spicy individual and people appreciate your artistic flair. You have discriminating taste: When it comes to making friends, you're very choosy. (Or is that chewsy?)

Best Friends

just one

walk by

a ton

Chocolate Chip

Your semi-sweet nature makes you a popular favorite. You combine a variety of good qualities into one delicious personality. Sometimes, though, you get a little nutty.

NEW GUY

say hi

museum

Sugar Cookie

You like to look as yummy as a sparkly sugar cookie. You are very social and fit in well at just about any occasion. Don't forget, a pretty surface isn't as important as the caloric sweetness inside.

FUN DAY OUT

beauty salon

8 ways to tell if your parents

True or False:

 1. Your parents often ask you to turn down your music.

 2. Their clothes are weirdly out of style.

 3. Sometimes you'll come into a room and catch them just sitting there, quietly, perhaps holding a book.

 4. They enjoy eating at least one of the following "foods": eggplant, anchovies, oysters, orange marmalade.

 5. During the winter, they keep the house uncomfortably cool. (Bonus point: When you complain, do they tell you to put on a sweater?)

 6. They completely over-react when your room is the tiniest bit messy.

 7. On more than one occasion, you have been embarrassed to be seen in public with them.

 8. They tell jokes that regular humans do not find funny.

SCORING

If you answered **true** to more than three of these questions, there is a good chance your parents are from a distant galaxy. Do not be alarmed. They come in peace.

Are you a big DORK?

Grab a piece of notepaper

For each activity, draw the shape that matches your enthusiasm level.

	Uh, no. I'd so never do that.	Maybe. Could be fun, I guess.	Awesome! I'm totally there!
Toast marshmallows around a campfire	☐	◇	♡
Ride a merry-go-round	☐	◇	♡
Run through sprinklers	☐	◇	♡
Blow soap bubbles in public	☐	◇	♡
Tell knock-knock jokes	☐	◇	♡
Do a goofy group dance at a wedding	☐	◇	♡
Start a pillow fight	☐	◇	♡
Wear a Halloween costume even though you won't be trick-or-treating	☐	◇	♡
Declare a thumb war	☐	◇	♡
Sing along to the car stereo	☐	◇	♡
Make snow angels	☐	◇	♡

SCORING

If most of your shapes are ♡ you are downright adorkable. Congrats — you're our kind of people. Others who describe themselves as dorks include Kirsten Dunst and Reese Witherspoon.

If most of your shapes are ◇ you are cool, with latent dorky tendencies. Don't be afraid to let the total dork inside you come out and play a little more often. You'll be glad you did.

If most of your shapes are ▢ you are super-cool. Too cool. Dead, maybe. Our advice? Enjoy life: Take a walk on the dork side.

If two shapes tie for first place, you're being difficult. Take the test again. This time, make shapes from the two high-scoring columns only.

What's your ROCK BAND

Say you and your friends are starting a band. Leaving aside questions of actual musical ability (mere technicalities), which instrument suits your personality best? Or should you be the lead singer?

personality?

Turn the page to find out about each band member's personality!

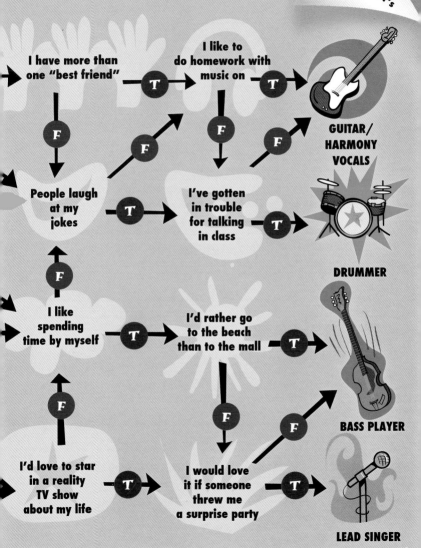

I have more than one "best friend" — **T** → I like to do homework with music on — **T** →

F ↓ ... **F** ↗ ... **F** ↓ ... **F** ↓

GUITAR/ HARMONY VOCALS

People laugh at my jokes — **T** → I've gotten in trouble for talking in class — **T** →

DRUMMER

F ↑

I like spending time by myself — **T** → I'd rather go to the beach than to the mall — **T** →

F ↑ ... **F** ↓ ... **F** ↗

BASS PLAYER

I'd love to star in a reality TV show about my life — **T** → I would love it if someone threw me a surprise party — **T** →

LEAD SINGER

SCORING

Guitar/Harmony Vocals
You're a multi-tasker, which is a fancy way of saying you can do two things at once — play the guitar and sing, for example. It's like rubbing your head and patting your tummy. Or braiding your hair and skydiving.

Drummer
You like sitting in the back of the class making jokes, or sitting in the back of the stage banging drums. Whether you're making your friends shake with laughter or shake it on the dance floor, you always rock.

Bass Player
You don't need to be in the spotlight, but you're so cool people pay attention to you anyway. Since you're basically un-freak-out-able, everybody counts on you to keep things grounded.

Lead Singer
Face it, you're a bit of a diva — which is a good thing for a lead singer to be. You are the center of your group and a natural leader. Just don't let all this pretend-garage-band glam go to your head.

MEET YOUR iNNER ARTiST!

TAKE SOME NOTEPAPER AND TRACE THE DRAWINGS BELOW. ADD THE MISSING PARTS TO DISCOVER THE ARTISTIC PERSONALITY YOU NEVER KNEW YOU HAD.

1. DRAW A TAIL FOR THIS CAT.

2. DRAW SOME EARS FOR THIS DOG.

3. DRAW WHAT IGOR IS EATING.

4. GIVE IVANA A FACE.

5. DESIGN IGBY'S SHIRT.

DRAWING CONCLUSIONS

TURN THE PAGE TO FIND OUT WHAT KIND OF ARTIST YOU ARE.

1 IS THE CAT TAIL YOU DREW

    A. STRAIGHT
    B. CURVED
    C. ZIG-ZAG
    D. FLUFFY

 2 ARE THE DOG EARS

    A. PERKY EARS THAT POINT UP
    B. LONG AND FLOWING
    C. CUTE AND FLOPPY
    D. DIFFERENT FROM EACH OTHER
       (ONE POINTS UP AND ONE
       DOWN, FOR EXAMPLE)

 3 IS IGOR EATING

    A. A SINGLE ITEM: A HAMBURGER, A CHICKEN LEG,
       SPAGHETTI, A SANDWICH, ETC.
    B. A MEAL COMPLETE WITH SIDE DISHES
    C. DESSERT
    D. SOMETHING NON-EDIBLE: A SHOE, A BOWLING BALL,
       A TELEPHONE, ETC. (IGOR'S COOL WITH THAT.
       HE'LL EAT ANYTHING.)

 4 IS IVANA

    A. SMILING WITH A CLOSED MOUTH
    B. SERIOUS, NO SMILE ("IVANA SMILE, BUT I CAN'T.")
    C. SMILING WITH AN OPEN MOUTH
    D. NONE OF THE ABOVE

 5 IGBY'S SHIRT HAS

    A. STRIPES
    B. A LOGO OR SLOGAN
    C. POLKA DOTS OR FLOWERS
    D. NONE OF THE ABOVE

WHAT KIND OF ARTISTIC PERSONALITY ARE YOU?

WHICH LETTER DID YOU MATCH MOST OFTEN?

A: CARTOONIST. You like to do things in a simple, straightforward style. You have a wide circle of friends who appreciate your quick wit. Your homework always gets turned in on time, just like a daily comic strip.

B: Portrait artist. You are thorough and have an eye for details. Friends turn to you for advice and really trust your thoughtful observations. You are truthful but kind, and always bring out the best in people.

C: Commercial artist. You're optimistic, cheerful and like to solve problems. People love hanging out with you and often follow your lead when deciding what to do for fun. You are very persuasive.

D: Fine artist. You are a creative free spirit. Not everyone understands you, but your close friends completely respect your individuality and unique style. You are the best kind of nutty.

YOUR LIFE AS A MOVIE

If your life were a movie, what kind of movie would it be — and would you pay $9.00 to see it?

1. Which of these signs would you hang on your bedroom door?
   a) I ♥ kittens
   b) I'd rather be skydiving
   c) Warning: Contents Under Pressure
   d) Private! Keep out! This means you!

2. If you could be a superstar athlete, which sport would you choose?
   a) basketball
   b) skateboarding
   c) figure skating
   d) gymnastics

3. You get a paper cut at school. What do you do?
   a) ask to go to the nurse's office. Immediately. Before you die.
   b) gross out your friends with your blo-o-o-o-od
   c) put a bandage on it
   d) pass out

4. Which fictional character would you most like to eat lunch with?
   a) Bart Simpson
   b) Cinderella
   c) Harry Potter
   d) James Bond

5. There's a nasty insect in the shower. You...
   a) squash it
   b) name it
   c) rescue it
   d) scream

6. You and your date want to make a big impression at the dance.
   How do you arrive?
   a) on a motorcycle
   b) in a horse-drawn carriage
   c) in a helicopter
   d) in the Oscar Meyer Wienermobile

7. Surprise! Your parents redecorated your room.
   The worst color they could paint your walls would be
   a) black
   b) plain white
   c) pink with flower stencils
   d) no new paint — they left the walls as is

Tally Your Score

1. a = 3	4. a = 2	6. a = 1
b = 1	b = 3	b = 3
c = 2	c = 4	c = 4
d = 4	d = 1	d = 2

2. a = 2		7. a = 3
b = 1	5. a = 1	b = 1
c = 3	b = 2	c = 2
d = 4	c = 3	d = 4
	d = 4	

3. a = 4
   b = 2
   c = 1
   d = 3

Turn the page for a special sneak
preview of the movie of your life.

What kind of movie would your life be? Add up all the points you got on the previous page. If you got...

7–11 points: an action-packed adventure
(like the Spider-Man movies)
You keep the thrills coming with your positive attitude and high energy. Your friends love the way you're totally up for anything. Whether today's stunt is bungee jumping or babysitting, you're always good to go.

12–17 points: a goofball comedy *(think Adam Sandler)*
All your life, you've been making a whole lot of funny. Friends know they can count on you for the perfect smart-aleck remark so, of course, the movie of your life would have them rolling in the aisles. Remember, they're not laughing <u>at</u> you, they're laughing <u>with</u> you.

18–22 points: an animated musical
(Beauty and the Beast, for example)
Your life would be the kind of movie where a guy and girl sing mushy songs and birds flutter and flowers bloom and little bunnies giggle and hide their eyes. It sounds too good to be true and, in fact, it is — but that doesn't stop you from dreaming. You're a true romantic and your friends wouldn't want it any other way.

23–28 points: an epic drama
(like the Lord of the Rings movies)
Hi, drama queen! (Oh, don't act like nobody's ever called you that before.) Your approach to life has all the sweeping emotion of an over-budget, over-the-top, cast-of-thousands extravaganza. Don't forget, though: A little boring can be a good thing sometimes.

Everyone knows that the choices you make define your character —
but did you ever wonder how, exactly? To find out, grab some notepaper and jot down
your choices as you navigate this chart. Then turn the page for enlightenment.

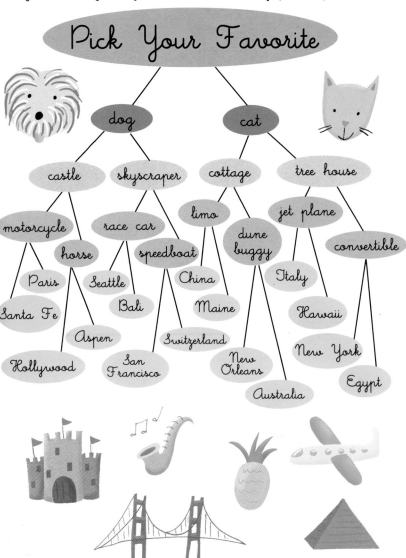

Pick Your Favorite

dog — cat

castle — skyscraper — cottage — tree house

motorcycle — race car — limo — jet plane

horse — speedboat — dune buggy — convertible

Paris — Seattle — China — Italy

Santa Fe — Bali — Maine — Hawaii

Aspen — Switzerland — New York

Hollywood — San Francisco — New Orleans — Egypt

Australia

Scoring

Fill in the blanks with your choices from page 21.

You might think this quiz would tell you this:

Someday you will have a pet _____?_____ , own a _____?_____ ,

travel by _____?_____ and live in _____?_____ .

But you'd be wrong. Here's what it really tells you:

You were a _____?_____ in a past life, you have a birthmark on your back

shaped like a _____?_____ , you sound like a _____?_____

when you snore and you have an evil twin living in _____?_____ .

Isn't it great to know that about yourself?

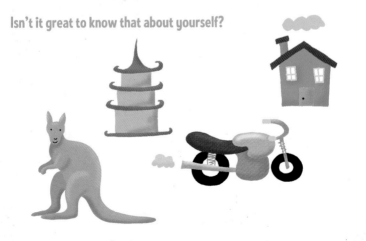

What's Your Superstar Name?

Just in case some Hollywood hotshot recognizes your mega-watt talent tomorrow, you'd better figure out your show biz name today.

FIRST NAME, PART 1

Find the number of your birthday month on this chart (January = 1, February = 2 and so on). The first part of your new name is in the column to the left of your birthday month.

An	1	reah
Sash	2	lia
Tay	3	asha
Star	4	lana
May	5	issa
Zan	6	ette
Lyn	7	lee
My	8	enna
Kat	9	thia
Lil	10	ya
Cyn	11	ique
Kay	12	elle

FIRST NAME, PART 2

Starting from the same row as your birthday month, count down the number of letters in your real middle name. (If you get to the end of the chart, just pop back up to the top and keep going.) When you're done counting, you'll find the second part of your new name in the column on the right.

LAST NAME

Take the last name of your all-time favorite teacher. It's the least you can do.

Now start practicing your new autograph, **Superstar!**

Your own personal
ANNOY-o-Meter

What really ticks you off? Are you a control freak? To find out, give each of these situations a score of 1 to 5: 1 for what annoys you LEAST, 5 for what annoys you MOST.

You made chocolate chip cookies for the bake sale but you must have used salt instead of sugar because... ick.

Your little brother skipped his chores this week and your parents never noticed.

Oh, what discomfiture! Today's the big vocab test and you totally forgot to study!

You bought a cute new top for a party but, when you get there, someone else is wearing the exact same thing.

You got caught chatting in class. Now you have to stay after to chat with the teacher.

You're on the phone with your crush when your little sib unplugs the line. On purpose.

You stayed out with friends later than planned. You get home to find the cat had a little accident on the carpet.

The theater is packed. Just as the movie starts, Huge McTallguy sits right in front of you.

Scoring

Look at the top three highest scores — the things that annoy you most.

If your three highest scores are all **REd** statements, you tend to get bugged by things outside your control. Even though you know there's not much you can do to change the situation, you still let it really get to you. Which, if you think about it, is pretty pointless. Try to let go of stuff you can't fix.

If your three highest scores are all **BLUE** statements, you're most annoyed by things within your control. You have great expectations for yourself and get frustrated when you don't meet your own super-high standards. Our advice? Loosen up. Be as forgiving of yourself as if you were your own best friend.

If your three high scores are a mix of **REd** and **BLUE** statements, you're someone who is annoyed by random things. How annoying.

What's the WRITE CAREER for You?

Analyze your handwriting to discover eight great career options you really should consider. It's easy: Just grab a piece of notepaper and write a couple lines of lyrics from your favorite song. Now look at your writing to answer the questions below.

1. How do the lines of writing appear on the page?

a *straight across* b *slanting down* c *slanting up*

If you picked...

... **a**, during the week you are very organized and disciplined. No one knows what you do on weekends. Be a **TEACHER**.

... **b**, you are upbeat about things going downhill. Be a **NEWSCASTER**.

... **c**, you are always enthusiastic and, like, way spirited. You're a total **CHEERLEADER**.

2. Which direction do your letters slant?

a *right* b *left* c *no slant*

If you picked...

... **a**, you are very caring, considerate and color-coordinated. Be a **FLIGHT ATTENDANT**.

... **b**, you cherish your alone time. Be an **ASTRONAUT**.

... **c**, you're extremely self-confident. But you knew that already. You ought to be a **MOVIE STAR**.

3. What size is your writing?

a tiny   **b** medium   **c** big

If you picked...

...**a**, you are detail-oriented and like to work in small spaces.
Be a **VALENTINE CANDY HEARTS WRITER**.

... **b**, you are a practical thinker, a good communicator
and just a little judgmental. So be a **JUDGE**.

... **c**, you are charismatic and crave lots of attention.
Be a **POLITICIAN**. (Handy tip: It's pronounced "nu-cle-ar.")

4. Flip the paper over and run your fingertips over the surface where you wrote.

a If you don't feel anything, you write with light pressure.

b If you feel some bumpiness, you write with medium pressure.

c If you feel high ridges and deep valleys, you write with heavy pressure.

If you picked...

...**a**, you are extremely sensitive and intuitive.
You have a future as a **FORTUNE TELLER**.

Or a **WEATHER FORECASTER**.

...**b**, you are practical, down-to-earth and methodical.
You'd be fab in a lab. Be a **SCIENTIST**.

...**c**, you are passionate, dramatic and, um,
really loud. (Ask anybody.)
Be an **OPERA SINGER**.

5. What do the upper loops of your letters look like?

a wide   **b** narrow   **c** no loops, just lines

If you picked...

...**a**, you have great creative vision and like to spend money. Be a **MOVIE DIRECTOR**.

...**b**, you are ambitious, resourceful and win most arguments. You should be a **LAWYER**. (Start today: Practice yelling "I object!" in class.)

...**c**, you like to get from point A to point B in the most direct way possible. You also like little bags of pretzels. Be a **PILOT**.

6. What do the lower loops of your letters look like?

a wide   **b** narrow   **c** no loops, just lines

If you picked...

...**a**, who wants to be a **MILLIONAIRE**? You do! (Okay, it's not really a career, but you'd be awfully good at it.)

...**b**, you have discriminating taste and don't mind sticky floors. Be a **MOVIE CRITIC**.

...**c**, you are organized and like to straighten things out. Be an **ORTHODONTIST**.

7. Where do you cross your t's?

a above the stem   **b** in the middle   **c** off to the side

If you picked...

...**a**, you have big dreams for the future, but you're not sure how to make them come true. Be a **SCIENCE FICTION WRITER**.

...**b**, you are confident within your regular routine and can handle life's ups and downs. You're a natural **TRAPEZE ARTIST**.

...**c**, you are impulsive and ready to go wherever the road takes you. Be a **TORNADO CHASER**.

8. How do you dot your i's and j's?

a with a dot (duh!)   **b** with a dash   **c** with a shape (circle, heart, star, etc.)

If you picked...

...**a**, you have an eye for detail and don't miss a thing. Be a **DETECTIVE**.

...**b**, you are always in a huge hurry, but sometimes it feels like you're just going around in circles. Be a **RACE CAR DRIVER**.

...**c**, you're totally into expressing your own style. You'd make a brilliant **FASHION DESIGNER**.

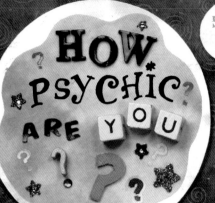

HOW PSYCHIC ARE YOU?

START HERE

Navigate the game board to find out how psychic you really are.

Which pet would you rather have?
• A cat named Harry (move up 1 space)
• A dog named Marian (move up 2 spaces)

Do you usually remember your dreams?
• No (move up 3 spaces)
• Yes (move up 2 spaces)

How did you do on your last pop quiz?
• I aced it (move up 2 spaces)
• I bombed (move up 1 space)
• I've never had a pop quiz (move back 1 space)

"Love at first sight" is
♥ Rare but wonderful (move up 2 spaces)
♥ Totally bogus (move up 3 spaces)

I can taste the difference between diet soda and regular soda.
• True (move up 2 spaces)
• False (move up 3 spaces)

Aries

SEMI SO-SO
You are kind of psychic. You can read your own mind.

NOT SO MUCH
You're not psychic, you're a sidekick, like Batman's Robin. Simple mistake.

TOTALLY!
You're not just psychic, you're spooky psychic. Promise you'll use those powers for good, okay?

Have you ever been thinking of a certain song right before it comes on the radio?
- Nope (move up 2 spaces)
- That's totally happened to me (move up 3 spaces)

My friend and I often say the exact same thing at the exact same time.
True - jinx!
(move up 1 space)
False
(move up 2 spaces)

QUICK - think of a number!
- It's 7 or over (move up 3 spaces)
- It's 6 or under (move up 2 spaces)

Which would be the worst?
- Not talking for a year (move up 3 spaces)
- Wearing a blindfold for a year (move up 2 spaces)
- No pizza for a year (move up 1 space)

LeO

6

five
5

8

Life Line
FaTe Line
HeaD Line
HeaRT Line

4

2

Cancer

7

DR. MOODITUDE'S

This quiz, devised by the mysterious Dr. Mooditude, is supposed to detect how you're feeling today. Will it work for you?

To find out, pick what you think is going on in each picture.

Dr Vera Mooditude

1 This guy is
a singing
b shouting

2 This clown is
a happy
b sad

3 This cat is
a dreaming
b scheming

4 This mushroom is
a regular size (the person is tiny)
b huge (the person is regular size)

PICTURE QUIZ

5 This person is
- **a** climbing up
- **b** sliding down

6 This dog is
- **a** on the inside looking out
- **b** on the outside looking in

7 This trick-or-treater is
- **a** smiling
- **b** serious

SCORING

If your answers were mostly a's:

Dr. Mooditude says, "You are feeling ambitious and optimistic today. You prefer to look on the bright side and tend to be outgoing with strangers. You feel secure and happy in your life right now."

If your answers were mostly b's:

Dr. Mooditude says, "You might be a little anxious or worried today. You are often shy around new people or unusual situations. You have a great imagination and can be very creative."

Is she right?

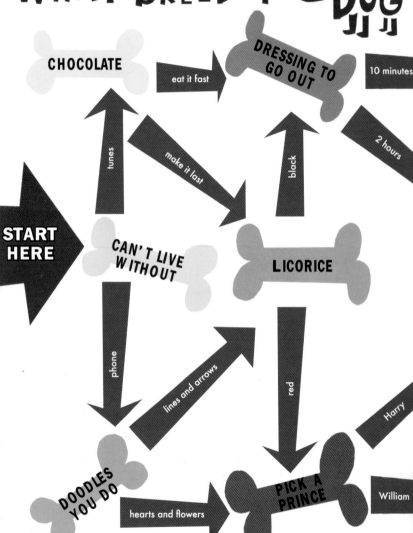

WHAT BREED OF DOG

CHOCOLATE — eat it fast → DRESSING TO GO OUT — 10 minutes

tunes

make it last

2 hours

black

START HERE → CAN'T LIVE WITHOUT

LICORICE

phone

lines and arrows

red

Harry

DOODLES YOU DO — hearts and flowers → PICK A PRINCE — William

ARE YOU?

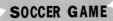

SOCCER GAME

I'll score us some goals →

GERMAN SHEPHERD
You're fierce, baby. You've got a strong competitive streak and a great sense of adventure. With your stamina, smarts and strong teeth, you can accomplish just about anything you put your mind to.

Come on, let's fly!

I'll score us some seats

SKY DIVING

JACK RUSSELL TERRIER
You're always playful and have a very quick wit. Everyday routines can make you fidgety — you have more energy than you know what to do with! You're a loyal friend and happily celebrate your buds' successes as if they were your own.

I'd rather die!

just get it done

CLOTHES SHOPPING

super fun

POODLE
Hello, gorgeous! You are the stylish sort who likes to look her best. Others may underestimate you, but inside that fuzzy head there's a blue-ribbon brain. You are living proof that looks and smarts can come in one adorable package.

What Would EMBARRASS You to Death?

Consider each pair of cringe-worthy choices and pick the more embarrassing one. Keep comparing humiliations until you're left with your own personal nightmare. (For extra potency, add the phrase "in front of your crush" to each option.)

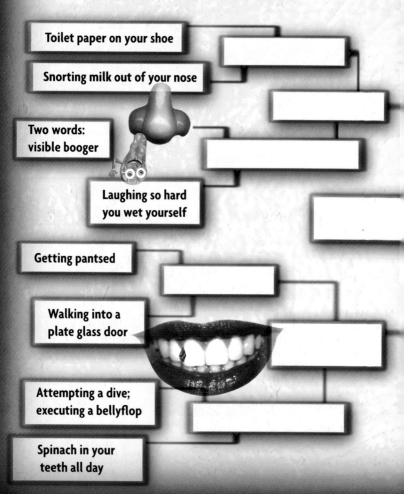

Toilet paper on your shoe

Snorting milk out of your nose

Two words: visible booger

Laughing so hard you wet yourself

Getting pantsed

Walking into a plate glass door

Attempting a dive; executing a bellyflop

Spinach in your teeth all day

Accidentally calling a teacher "Mom"

Trip, fall, sprawl in the hall

Losing part of your bathing suit

That bad smell? Came from you.

Unleashing a loud, stinky burp in class

A really, really bad haircut

Your skirt is tucked up, not hanging down

Is that bird poop on your head?

CREDITS

Design and Art Coordination:
Cindy Friedman
Art Direction: Jill Turney

Filled in the Blanks: Paula Hannigan
Pop Quiz: John Cassidy
Lettering, pages 30–31: Liz Hutnick

Illustration by:

Ben Fishman

Karen Johnson

Brian Biggs

Linda Solovic

Julia Gran

Marcos Sorenson

Michael Wertz

Thanks to:

Chelsea, Erin, Laura, Laurel, Marielle, Megan, Nicole, Nora, Rachel, Sarah, Sasha, Ying and all the test testers at Klutz. Special thanks to Marilyn Green.

If you enjoyed **It's All About Me**, check out **Me and My Friends: The Book of Us** by the editors of Klutz.

More Great Books from Klutz

My Fabulous Life in Pictures
My Life According to Me®
Picture Bracelets
Friendship Bracelets

My Anytime Anywhere Autograph Book
Nail Art
Velvet Art
Decorate Your Locker
Dial with Style™